KU-361-255

Brown Bear Wood

if you go Down to the Woods Today

Poems by
Rachel Piercey

Illustrated by
Freya Hartas

MAGIC CAT PUBLISHING

MAGIC CAT
PUBLISHING

If You Go Down to the Woods Today © 2021 Magic Cat Publishing Ltd
Text © 2021 Rachel Piercey
Illustrations © 2021 Freya Hartas
"Teddy Bear's Picnic" Words and Music by John W Bratton, Jimmy Kennedy © 1932,
Reproduced by permission of B Feldman & Co Ltd, M Witmark & Sons & EMI Music Publishing, London W1F 9LD
First Published in 2021 by Magic Cat Publishing Ltd
The Milking Parlour, Old Dungate Farm, Plaistow Road, Dunsfold, Surrey GU8 4PJ, UK

A catalogue record for this book is available from the British Library.

ISBN 978-1-913520-05-2

The illustrations were drawn in pencil and coloured digitally
Set in Bentham, La Parisienne, Lancelot and Sevillana

Published by Rachel Williams and Jenny Broom
Designed by Nicola Price
Edited by Helen Brown and Rachel Williams

Manufactured in China, TLF0121

3 5 7 9 8 6 4 2

MIX
Paper from
responsible sources
FSC® C104723
FSC
www.fsc.org

Hello! I'm Bear! Can we be friends?

I'd love it if we could.

Perhaps you'd like to see my home,

the world inside the wood?

SPRING BRINGS NEW LIFE
BEAR'S WORLD AWAKES

Spring is waking up the world!
Will you come with me?
My woodland home is full of friends,
let's peek inside and see...

The winter months were long and cold,
the ground was hard with ice.
But now the grassy floor's alive
with rabbits, deer and mice.

We've woken up to gold and green,
the air is smelling sweet.
We're starting to explore again,
to stretch our tails and feet.

My woodland's full of animals,
of every different kind.
So shall we stay here for a while
and see what we can find?

What to spot in Bear's world

- **BEAR** wandering the wood
- **SKUNK** snoozing under a bush
- **BLUEBELLS** pushing up their heads
- **BABY CHIPMUNK** in a hammock
- **SNAKE** enjoying the spring sunshine
- **BLUE TITS** building their nest
- **PROFESSOR OWL** trying to sleep
- **RED ADMIRAL BUTTERFLY** sipping nectar
- **MAMA WEASEL** wheeling a wheelbarrow
- Two **BIRDS** returning from their winter break
- Five brown **BABY MICE**, many ready to explore
- Two **CATERPILLARS** saying "hello"
- **GREY SQUIRREL** swinging through the air

HOME SWEET HOME

All of us are busy now,
settling into home:
bringing, building, burrowing,
and making it our own.

A tree for Owl, a log for Frog,
a web for spinning Spider,
a hole dug from the earth for Fox,
her rusty cubs beside her.

Each tree can host a hundred rooms,
with roots to hide beneath,
with hidey-holes inside the bark,
and boughs where creatures sleep.

And everywhere the sun and sky
grow from the ground as well,
in dazzling yellow daffodils,
in blue and breezy bells.

What to spot in Bear's home

○ BEAR decorating his den with beautiful flowers from the woodland

○ WEASEL poking her head out of a log

○ MAMA WREN and PAPA WREN gathering sticks to build their nest

○ SPIDER spinning a special sign

○ A FOX CUB who has gone wandering

○ FROG dusting his home

○ ANT climbing a staircase

GRANDMA BAT and GRANDPA BAT roosting upside-down

RACCOON'S leaf-lined bed

MOUSE riding piggyback

BUNNIES sweeping the entrance

RED and GREY SQUIRRELS zipping down a tree-root slide

PAPA BEAR collecting flowers

Four NESTS full of eggs

FAWNS watering some bluebells

RED ADMIRAL BUTTERFLY on MAMA DEER'S velvety nose

SCHOOL DAYS

It's time for school inside the wood,
to come and learn together,
and make a whole new group of friends
with fur or shells or feathers.

Our classroom is a hollow trunk,
our playground is close by.
Our teachers pad from underground
or dart in from the sky.

We learn the moon, we feel the sun,
we read the changing trees,
we keep a record of the pond,
make music from the breeze.

And all the different animals
look after one another:
new-to-school, or oldest-here,
neighbours, sisters, brothers.

LEAVES

BRANCHES

NEST

TRUNK

ROOTS

SWEET PEAS

CABBAGES

POTATOES

What to spot at school

- BEAR reciting poetry to his classmates
- MAMA SQUIRREL teaching the animals how to count
- PROFESSOR OWL giving a lesson on the moon
- A lively game of HOPSCOTCH
- SPARROW leading a chirping, cheeping choir
- SPIDER teaching the alphabet
- Three CATERPILLARS looking at leaves very closely
- A NEW STUDENT, here for the summer months, being made welcome
- A WOODLAND MAP
- Four WOODPECKER CHICKS listening in from home
- A VEGETABLE PATCH
- NANA RABBIT helping the students make wind chimes
- FROG teaching a science lesson by the pond

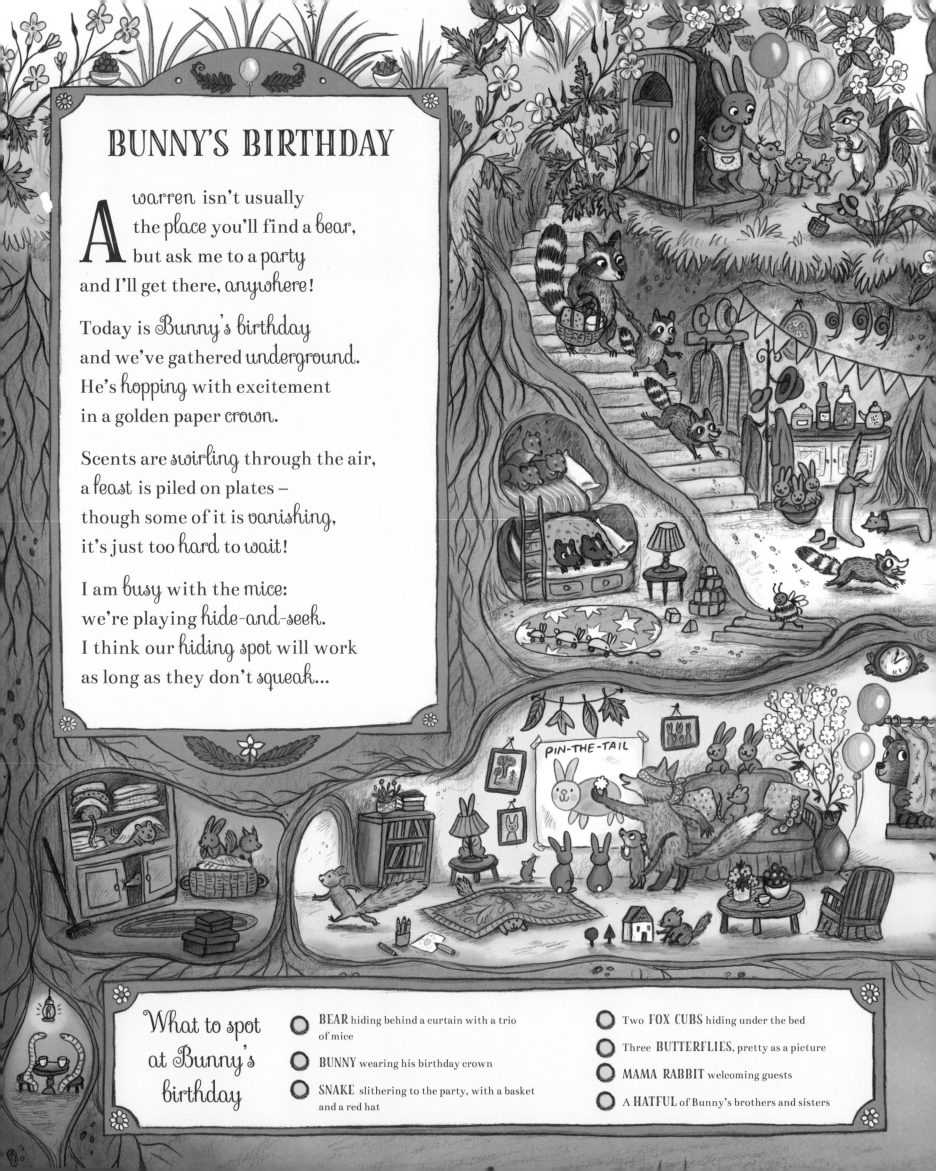

BUNNY'S BIRTHDAY

A warren isn't usually
the place you'll find a bear,
but ask me to a party
and I'll get there, anywhere!

Today is Bunny's birthday
and we've gathered underground.
He's hopping with excitement
in a golden paper crown.

Scents are swirling through the air,
a feast is piled on plates –
though some of it is vanishing,
it's just too hard to wait!

I am busy with the mice:
we're playing hide-and-seek.
I think our hiding spot will work
as long as they don't squeak...

PIN-THE-TAIL

What to spot
at Bunny's
birthday

○ **BEAR** hiding behind a curtain with a trio
of mice

○ **BUNNY** wearing his birthday crown

○ **SNAKE** slithering to the party, with a basket
and a red hat

○ Two **FOX CUBS** hiding under the bed

○ Three **BUTTERFLIES**, pretty as a picture

○ **MAMA RABBIT** welcoming guests

○ A **HATFUL** of Bunny's brothers and sisters

NANA RABBIT putting the finishing touches on the birthday cake

A pile of PRESENTS and CARDS

A game of PIN-THE-TAIL

Three topsy-turvy SNAILS

Two BABY WEASELS wriggling into wellies

A plate of wibbly-wobbly JELLY

PAPA RABBIT pinning up bunting

Two bouncing BEES

Shelves of yellow CHICKS

SUMMER BRINGS THE SUN
SPORTS DAY

The days are long and balmy now,
the sun climbs higher and higher.
Trees are thick with glossy leaves,
like flicks of emerald fire.

And what a perfect day for sport:
for races up and down,
and back and forth, and fast and slow,
in air and on the ground.

From the sidelines, families watch
to clap and cheer their crew,
refreshing us with picnic treats
and cups of morning dew.

Who will win the running race?
Whose the furthest throw?
Who can jump the highest, longest?
Ready, get set, GO!

What to spot at sports day

- BEAR stretching in a yellow bib to prepare for the games
- A SIX-LEGGED RACE
- A LEAF PARACHUTE competition
- A whooshing game of STICK THROWING
- Pink and yellow DOG ROSES and HONEYSUCKLE
- PICNICS, high and low
- TROPHIES and ROSETTES on display
- A sky-high RELAY RACE
- Two HIGH JUMP competitions
- A very slow SNAIL and SLUG RACE
- PAPA DEER and MAMA FOX launching into the long jump
- A TUG-OF-WAR between families
- Two WOODPECKERS pecking the same tree, head-to-head

HIGH SUMMER

The sun is right above my head,
the air is silky-warm.
The rustle-bustle bushy leaves
have many shapes and forms.

And up here there are leaping legs,
and claws that cling on tight.
And up here there are tails which trail
through dazzling, dappled light.

Just listen! You can hear the birds,
they coo and sing nearby.
Just watch! That funny-looking leaf
unfolds a butterfly.

He sunbathes on the bark a while,
enjoying his new home,
while round him, bugs and beetles crawl
and gleam like precious stones.

What to spot in high summer

- A cheeky **CATERPILLAR** tickling **BEAR**
- **GREY SQUIRRELS** playing chase
- **MAMA MOUSE** and **PAPA MOUSE** reading
- The **PIGEON FAMILY** singing for joy
- **SPIDER** spinning her lacy web
- **GRANDMA BAT** and **GRANDPA BAT** fast asleep
- **PROFESSOR OWL** having her nap interrupted
- Two smiling **RACCOONS**
- **BEAR'S LITTLE SISTER** climbing a tree
- **MICE** playing frisbee
- **BEES** performing acrobatics in the sky
- Five **BEETLES**, red as rubies, on one leaf
- Three **BUTTERFLIES** emerging from their chrysalises

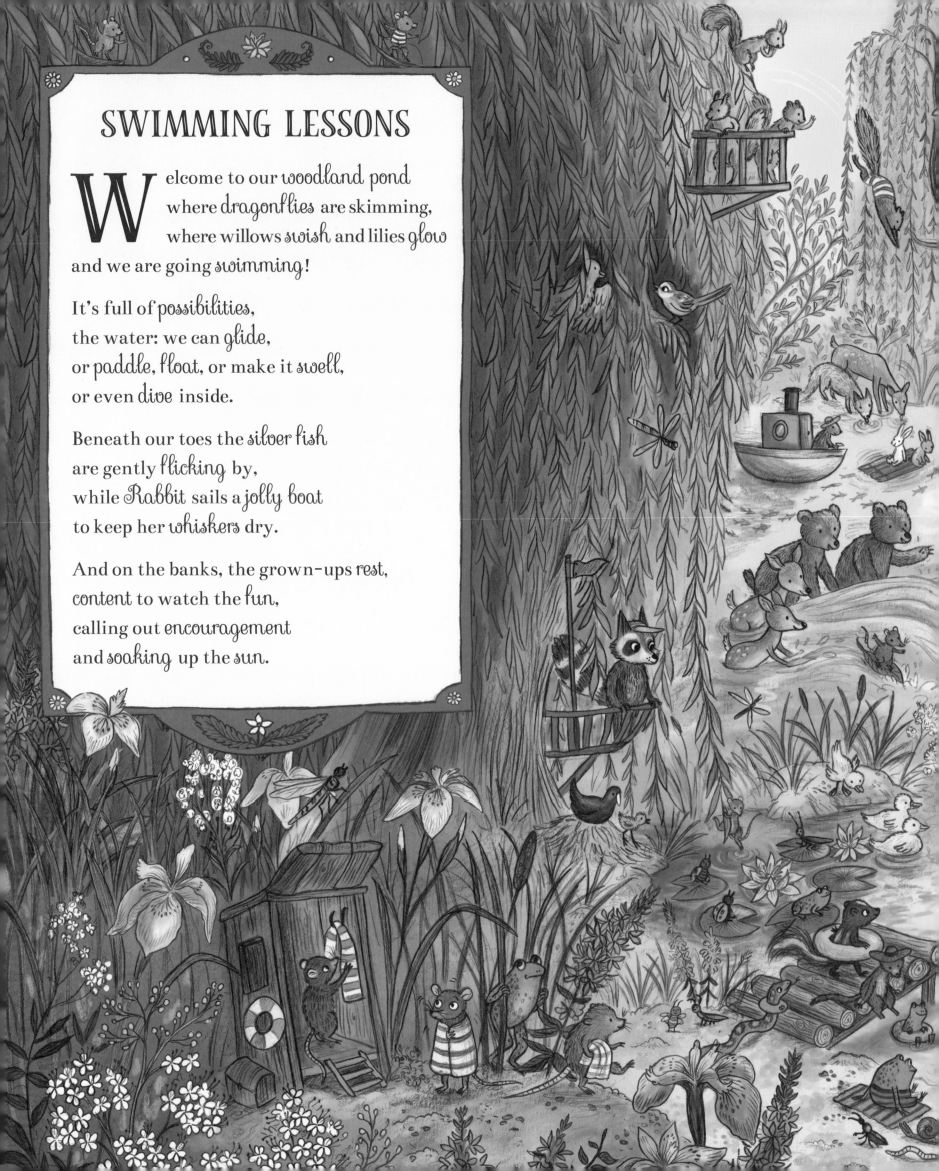

SWIMMING LESSONS

Welcome to our woodland pond
where dragonflies are skimming,
where willows swish and lilies glow
and we are going swimming!

It's full of possibilities,
the water: we can glide,
or paddle, float, or make it swell,
or even dive inside.

Beneath our toes the silver fish
are gently flicking by,
while Rabbit sails a jolly boat
to keep her whiskers dry.

And on the banks, the grown-ups rest,
content to watch the fun,
calling out encouragement
and soaking up the sun.

What to spot during swimming lessons

- BEAR drying off after his swim
- A shy FROG
- Two SHOALS of FISH
- PROFESSOR OWL and RACCOON watching over the swimmers
- MOUSE dipping her toe into the water
- FOX CUBS playing chase
- BEAR'S LITTLE BROTHER, BEAR'S LITTLE SISTER and the FAWNS making waves
- GRANDPA TOAD watching over his grandchildren
- MAMA FOX and MAMA DEER drinking the swimming pool
- PAPA BEAR and PAPA DEER enjoying a thermos of tea
- MAMA WEASEL'S book club
- MAMA RABBIT in a captain's hat
- A diving SQUIRREL

BEAR'S PICNIC

Today's the kind of balmy day
when all you want to do
is picnic under summer skies,
as clouds drift into view.

A bag or basket, faded rug,
a favourite floppy hat,
some food, some friends, a ball or two:
you don't need more than that.

We've found ourselves a lovely spot,
with sunshine, shade and flowers.
We've spread the rugs and spread the food,
we'll dawdle here for hours.

For picnics are the perfect place
for doing what you love:
to talk or read or snooze or play,
or all of the above!

What to spot at Bear's picnic

- BEAR eating a bowl of **WILD STRAWBERRIES**
- MICE and CHIPMUNKS playing catch
- SWIMMING COSTUMES drying on a mossy log
- A FOX CUB swinging her bat
- NANA RABBIT under a sunshade
- A refreshing **PADDLING POOL**
- A FAWN helping the others stay cool
- Fourteen different HATS
- A mostly hidden MOUSE
- A speedy PICNIC BASKET
- A HANDSTAND and a CARTWHEEL
- Three friends making **DAISY CHAINS**
- An ICE CREAM stand

PUTTING ON A PLAY

I love the atmosphere and sound
of speeches and instructions,
as our animal-dramatics group
prepares the next production!

The play is quite a famous one,
by Shakespeare: full of dreams,
with love and laughter, magic spells,
a fairy king and queen.

Some animals like nothing more
than dressing up to act:
the thrill of playing someone else,
the thrill of being clapped!

Others star behind the scenes
and help in different ways:
making costumes, painting sets
and dressing up the stage.

What to spot in the play

- BEAR and WEASEL helping the stars to twinkle
- The FAIRY KING and FAIRY QUEEN wearing handmade crowns
- GRANDPA TOAD making tickets, with a little help from his friends
- MAMA FOX and MAMA WEASEL painting
- A not-very-fierce LION
- Two BUNNIES teetering on stilts
- SPIDER spinning a silken spell

NANA RABBIT and PAPA RACCOON making costumes

A GRIN and a FROWN

PAPA BEAR wearing donkey's ears

A FOX CUB with a bottle of magic potion

PROFESSOR OWL decorating the theatre

Two CATERPILLARS munching sweet berries

MAMA MOUSE directing the play from a great height

MAMA SQUIRREL and PAPA MOUSE offering refreshments to cast and crew

A loud BAND making an entrance

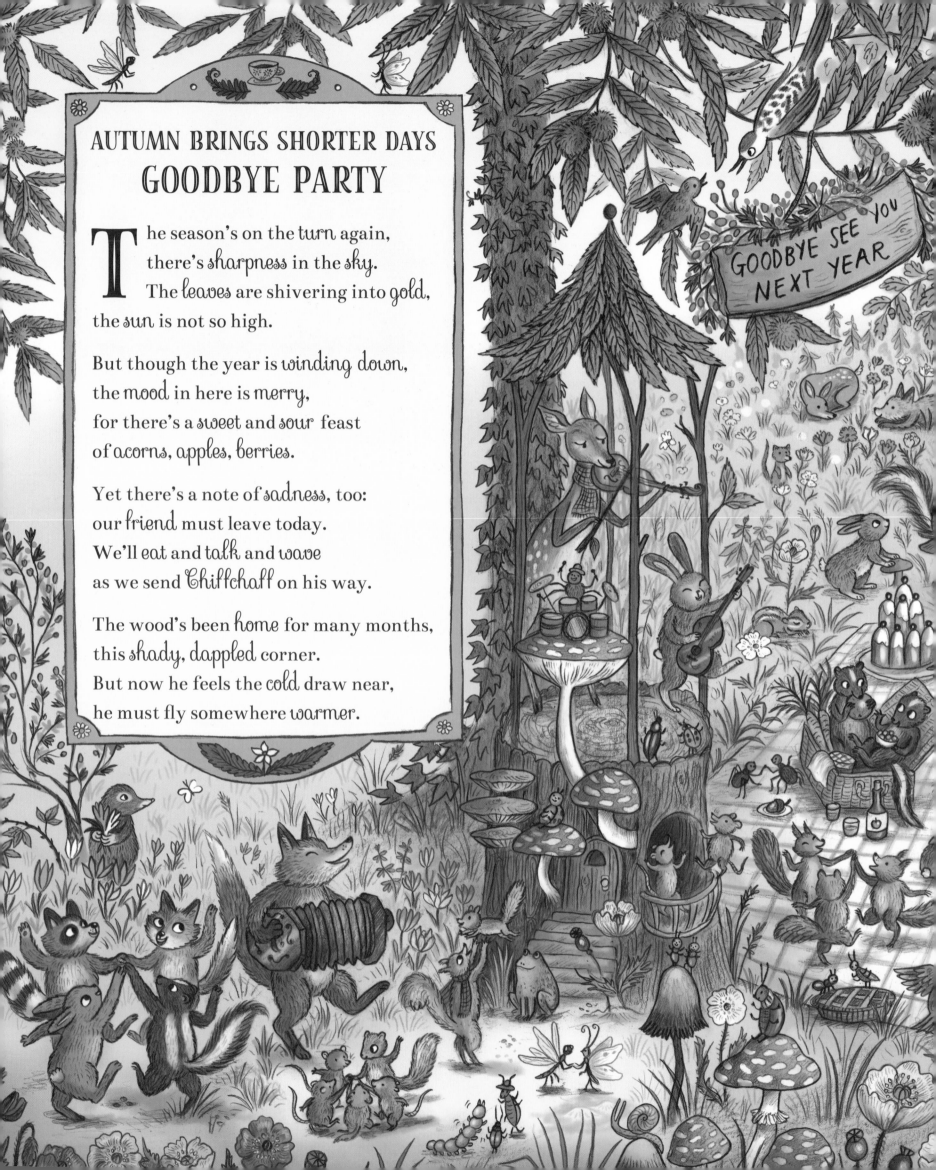

AUTUMN BRINGS SHORTER DAYS
GOODBYE PARTY

The season's on the turn again,
there's sharpness in the sky.
The leaves are shivering into gold,
the sun is not so high.

But though the year is winding down,
the mood in here is merry,
for there's a sweet and sour feast
of acorns, apples, berries.

Yet there's a note of sadness, too:
our friend must leave today.
We'll eat and talk and wave
as we send Chiffchaff on his way.

The wood's been home for many months,
this shady, dappled corner.
But now he feels the cold draw near,
he must fly somewhere warmer.

GOODBYE SEE YOU NEXT YEAR

What to spot at the goodbye party

- BEAR taking a rest on PAPA BEAR
- A lovely GIFT from some of the young animals
- Red, white and yellow POPPIES
- Five TAILS under the tablecloth
- CHIFFCHAFF, the guest of honour, enjoying the party
- A garland of red HAWTHORN BERRIES
- Two SQUIRRELS burying acorns
- PAPA MOUSE telling a very funny joke
- MAMA WEASEL lost in a book
- A FOX CUB and a FAWN taking a break from the bustle of the party
- The members of the WOODLAND BAND
- A cake decorated with juicy BLACKBERRIES
- Seven red-and-white TOADSTOOLS

RAINY DAY

The rain is pouring down today,
each drop a splashy thud.
The grassy, earthy woodland floor
is now a sea of mud.

A group of damp explorers
have set out to brave the skies,
to jump and stamp in puddles
and make sticky, brown mud pies.

Some, like me, have stayed inside:
we do not wish our toes
or tails or fur to ooze with mud,
we'd rather chat or doze.

And other friends are dreamy,
watching drops of liquid light,
which glimmer on the leaves
and make the cloudy wood seem bright.

What to spot on a rainy day

- BEAR catching a leak
- Seven SNAILS having fun in the rain
- An upside-down NEST being used for shelter
- SPIDER'S WEB draped in diamonds
- BEETLES with leafy umbrellas
- PAPA SKUNK snoozing in a hollow tree
- FROG, TOAD and MICE jumping into puddles
- BUNNIES having a water fight
- WEASELS and RACCOON making mud pies
- The DEER FAMILY with a pile of apples
- SNAKE, BEAR'S LITTLE BROTHER and BAT gazing at raindrops
- Red-orange ROSE HIPS
- MAMA WOODPECKER and PROFESSOR OWL enjoying a hot chocolate

ART CLASS

The sharpness in the air
creates a feeling hard to name.
The trees are orange, scarlet, gold,
each leaf a tongue of flame.

And living in this autumn world,
which glows inside the heart,
inspires my friends and I to try
our paws at works of art.

Each artist dreams of building up
their own unique creation,
and fills the paper, clay or cloth
with wild imagination.

Each piece is different to the next:
the colours, styles and scenes,
and how it makes you feel inside
and what you think it means.

ART
EXHIBITION

What to spot during the art class

- **BEAR** dreaming up ideas for his next piece of art
- **RED ADMIRAL BUTTERFLY** being a model for the day
- A bowl of **FRUIT** and **NUTS**
- **FOX CUBS** painting a picture with their paws
- **NANA RABBIT** admiring **BUNNY'S** drawing
- **BEAR'S LITTLE SISTER** preparing to start again
- A sculpture made of **TWIGS**
- **RACCOON** crafting a special jug
- **MICE** with needles and thread
- **FROG** painting a vase of flowers
- A multicoloured **SKUNK**
- **WOODPECKER'S** beak in an unusual place
- The **DEER FAMILY** posing for a portrait

BEAR'S CAMPFIRE

Against the velvet of the sky,
the fire's a leap of light:
a sun that's settled on the earth,
a hypnotising sight.

We huddle round the swaying flames
for tales and roasted treats.
We talk and sing and warm our paws
with chestnuts, hot and sweet.

For Owl and Bat, it's daytime now,
and they are wide awake:
each creature swoops amongst the stars,
a smoky, ghostly shape.

But other friends are getting tired:
it's nearly time for bed.
And round the campfire, there are many
bobbing... nodding... heads.

What to spot at Bear's campfire

- BEAR telling a thrilling campfire story
- Two MOLES perched on their molehills
- A pile of SWEET CHESTNUTS ready for roasting
- Three swooping BATS
- FROG having a bath to keep cool
- TOAD hidden under a pile of leaves
- SPIDER'S golden web
- RACCOONS and MICE enjoying the warmth
- FAWN playing the fiddle
- BIRDS roosting in the trees
- PROFESSOR OWL wide awake
- Three sleeping SKUNKS
- MAMA FOX dancing with her CUBS
- Five FIREFLIES
- A glowing CRESCENT MOON

WINTER BRINGS THE COLD
WINTER SPORTS

The sun is lower in the sky
and many trees are bare.
The snowflakes spiral silently
through peaceful silver air.

The wood is not so quiet, though:
it rings with rowdy glee.
We've all met up, with chattering teeth,
to sled and skate and ski.

We teeter, totter, twirl and glide,
make angels in the snow.
We slide around the icy trees
and dodge the mistletoe.

And when our toes are truly cold,
we gulp a steaming drink.
Then out again to seize the day
before the sun can sink!

What to spot during winter sports

- BEAR skating on a frozen pond
- A RACE through the winter branches
- Three SNOW ANGELS
- Skiing SKUNKS
- MICE tangled up in a ball of mistletoe
- A SNOWBALL FIGHT
- Four branches dripping with ICICLES
- Half of MAMA FOX
- Three SQUIRRELS searching for and digging up acorns
- A SNOW DEER
- BUNNIES bundled onto a sled
- Red HOLLY BERRIES and black IVY BERRIES
- The PIGEON FAMILY making prints in the snow

BEAR'S WINTER FEAST

In the depths of wintertime,
a feast is just the thing
to raise our chilly spirits,
with a chance to eat and sing!

We've gathered sprigs of holly
to make ruby-studded wreaths,
and garlanded the empty boughs
with green and russet leaves.

Around the heaving tables
sit a heap of happy guests.
We're sharing songs of snow and fire,
and merry yarns, and jests.

The winter sun is setting fast:
it never reached full height.
But we will linger on here
in this jolly, joyful night.

What to spot
at Bear's
winter feast

- **BEAR** wearing a leaf and berry crown
- A **MAP** of the woods
- Three **MICE** performing in special costumes
- **BUNNY, FAWN** and a **FOX CUB** making garlands
- **RACCOONS** and **MICE** greeting their visitors
- A game of **DOMINOS**
- **PAPA DEER'S** decorated antlers

A nearly completed JIGSAW PUZZLE

A PUPPET THEATRE show

A book of SONGS

An indoor BOWLING ALLEY

CHIPMUNK perching on a pie

Four HOLLY WREATHS

A very hungry SKUNK

The winter SUN low in the sky

The SQUIRREL FAMILY being generous with their acorns

GOODNIGHT WORLD
BEAR'S DEN

The year is getting sleepy now,
the night is getting on.
It's way beyond my bedtime:
do excuse this giant yawn!

Everyone has said goodnight,
sleep tight and see you soon.
And now I'm in my cosy den
beneath the gentle moon.

I plan to sleep, like many friends,
until the start of spring,
dozing through the frozen weeks
that frosty winter brings.

The year will wake again, in time,
to warmer, brighter skies.
But now we need to rest and dream,
so shhh and close your eyes.

What to spot in Bear's den

○ **BEAR** cuddling his teddy

○ A patchwork **BLANKET** to snuggle under

○ A **SNOWGLOBE** placed on the shelf

○ Bunk beds full of **BUNNIES**

○ Yellow-striped **PYJAMAS**

○ Camouflaged **SNAIL SHELLS**

○ Shelves full of **BOOKS**

○ A snuffed-out **CANDLE**

○ Fluffy **SKUNK TAILS** poking out of their den

○ A hammock full of cosy **CHIPMUNKS**

○ Four **BATS** sleeping peacefully upside-down

○ Two toy **RABBITS** tucked close to their owners

○ Two **MOLES** dozing inside their molehill

○ **SNAKE** snoring on the root of a tree

○ Rows of roosting **BIRDS**

○ **PROFESSOR OWL** watching over her friends

NATURE TRAIL

Nature is everywhere. It's up in the air, under the ground and all around us. We only need to look. Here are some ideas for you to explore and get creative outside...

These nature-inspired illustrations were hidden in Bear's world. Did you spot them?

Turn back the pages and revisit the woodland to try to find them.

Flowering trees

Many trees flower in spring. Sometimes the flowers are eye-catching, like this pretty pink blossom. But sometimes you have to look more closely at the tree to see them. Can you find three different types of flowering trees? Are any of them pink?

Tree stump

Tree stumps are often full of life. Even new trees can grow from a stump! Next time you come across one, take a good look. You might not see a woodland school – but are there any insects, plants or fungi?

Birds singing

The longer, lighter days of spring encourage male birds to start singing in their quest to find a partner. Each species of bird has a unique song – sit quietly outside one morning and tune into how many different calls you can hear. Ask an adult to help you write down the sounds of their songs – you'll probably end up with some unusual letter combinations!

Nests

Lots of birds build their nests in spring. Some birds will only have one egg, and others can have as many as fifteen! Look up into the trees around you – can you spot any twiggy, grassy nests?

Burrows

Rabbits create burrows underground. Next time you're out and about, look for tell-tale holes dug into the earth – there might be someone living underneath your feet! Make up a name for them and tell someone a short story about what they're doing right now.

SUMMER BRINGS THE SUN

Creepy-crawlies

Ants, caterpillars, crickets, woodlice, ladybirds and bees are all 'arthropods' – this means their skeleton is on the outside and their body is made of segments. Look at all the different shapes and colours! Go outside and pay close attention – can you see or hear one of these little creatures? Will it stay in one place long enough for you to draw it?

Leaf shapes

Leaves come in varied shapes, sizes and forms. Some are glossy and some are hairy. Some are long and thin like needles and some are shaped a bit like stars. Some are smooth at the edges and some have jagged teeth. Collect as many differently-shaped fallen leaves as you can find, then present your own science show, holding up and describing your favourite leaves.

Flying insects

Is there a pond, lake or river near you? Then there are probably hundreds of flying insects! They are so light and lacy, it's often easy to miss them. Sit quietly for a few minutes, looking around and over the water. Can you spot the largest and the smallest flying insects?

Rough bark

Each species of tree has a particular type of bark: shiny, rough, light, dark, striped, scaly... Bark is satisfying to touch: close your eyes and press your hands gently against different trees. Can you think of a word to describe how they feel? You might like to take out some paper and pencils to make bark rubbings.

Fruit in season

Different fruits grow at different times of the year. Next time you're at the shops or the market, ask someone who works there which fruits are in season – this generally means they'll be grown in the country where you live. You might find strawberries or blackberries there!

AUTUMN BRINGS SHORTER DAYS

Something spiky

There are lots of spiky things in the natural world – the spikes discourage animals from having a nibble! Can you find anything that looks spiky on your next walk? You could try writing an acrostic poem where each line begins with one of the letters of the word 'SPIKY'.

Red toadstools

There are so many richly reddish-coloured things in autumn, like red toadstools. How many red things can you spot? Remember to look up and down as well as side to side. Are they all the same kind of red?

Colourful leaves

Autumn is famous for its vividly colourful leaves. You might see red, orange, yellow, brown, purple or pink colours. Collect the most beautiful fallen leaves you can find and arrange them into a pattern on the grass. Then take a photograph of your natural artwork!

Spider's webs

Spider's webs look delicate and are easily broken if you're not careful. But if you had an equal weight of spider silk and steel, the spider silk would be stronger! Take some pens and pencils when you next venture outside and draw a spider's web, taking care not to disturb its creator.

Starry nights

The days grow shorter in autumn and this means that you can see the stars earlier. For thousands of years, humans have told stories about the stars. Go outside with an adult and pick a shining cluster. Can you see any shapes in there? Make up a story about these stars and tell it to the person you're with.

Clouds

If the weather is cold and the air is not too dry, your breath can make a white cloud as you breathe out. This is the natural water vapour in your breath turning into tiny droplets of water or ice as it hits the air. Have fun making cloud shapes the next time the weather is cold!

Bare trees

Trees that lose their leaves in winter are called 'deciduous'. They make beautiful silhouettes against the winter sky. Pick your favourite bare trees and try to imitate their shape with your body.

Acorns ahoy!

Squirrels bury nuts in autumn, to dig up and eat in the winter when it's harder to find food. Have you seen any squirrels scrabbling to find buried treats near you? What about other wild animals who are active in winter – what do they eat?

Animal tracks

Have you ever woken up to a blanket of snow, punctured by crisp animal footprints? It's an amazing sight! If you look closely at muddy or frosty ground, you might be able to see some tracks there as well. Examine the size and shape. Can you guess which animal made them?

The moon

Our glowing moon looks like different shapes all the time. A new moon is invisible, then it grows in size – waxes – until it's full, and then decreases in size – wanes – until it's invisible again. If you look outside over the course of a month, you will see these changes in the sky above you. Which is your favourite shape?

NATURE RESOURCES

If you'd like to find out more about the natural world, here are some suggested sites for you to explore with an adult.

Audubon for Kids
This gorgeous website brings the bird world closer, with facts, games, art ideas and other activities.

audubon.org/get-outside/activities/audubon-for-kids

The Conversation for Kids – Seasons
This smart website takes questions from kids and answers them thoroughly and thoughtfully. Here, two scientists answer a question about the seasons.

theconversation.com/curious-kids-why-are-there-different-seasons-at-specific-times-of-the-year-109380

Defenders of Wildlife
This conservation organisation aims to protect wildlife across North America. Wander around their website to learn more about North American plants and animals and their hugely different habitats.

defenders.org

Kew Gardens
Kew Gardens is a famous botanical site where specialists grow and study incredible plants from all over the world. Find out more about the science of botany through videos, activities and challenges.

kew.org/learning

The Kids Should See This
This is a beautiful time-lapse video of a wood in America over the seasons. Watch it when you feel like taking the time to slow down.

thekidsshouldseethis.com/post/a-forest-year

National Geographic Kids
Animal facts, quizzes, interviews and some wonderful photographs make this a rich resource.

natgeokids.com

The Wildlife Trusts
As well as being packed with fascinating information on different species, this site has a series of live camera feeds, offering an exciting up-close look at the lives of owls, ospreys, puffins and many others!

wildlifetrusts.org

The Woodland Trust
This website helps you identify different species of trees by looking closely at their buds, bark, leaves and flowers. Being able to name trees is a great way of feeling connected to the world around you.

woodlandtrust.org.uk

POETRY RESOURCES

If you'd like to find out more about poems and poetry, here are some suggested sites for you to explore with an adult.

The Centre for Literacy in Primary Education's PoetryLine
This lovely website is packed full of poems, learning resources – including a useful glossary of poetic terms – poetry performances and poet interviews.

clpe.org.uk/poetryline

The Children's Poetry Archive
This is a treasure trove of audio recordings of poems. Hearing a poet read their own work really brings it to life. You can search by theme and age, and you'll get a special peek into how and why the poets wrote their poems.

childrens.poetryarchive.org

Poetry 180
Set up by US poet laureate Billy Collins, Poetry 180 makes it easy for children to hear or read a poem each day of the 180 days of the school year.

loc.gov/poetry/180

The Poetry Foundation
The American Poetry Foundation has a wealth of children's poems, as well as some magical poem films.

poetryfoundation.org/learn/children

Poetry Minute
Created by US children's poet laureate Kenn Nesbitt, each of the poems on this website can be read in about one minute and the site provides a new poem for each day of the school year.

poetryminute.org

Poetry Out Loud
With plenty of poets and collections to browse, these poems can be performed out loud, shared with others or simply read in your head.

poetryoutloud.org

The Poetry Society
The UK Poetry Society has a great website called Poetry Class, with poetry lessons and activities on a whole variety of themes. These resources will guide you through writing your very own poem!

resources.poetrysociety.org.uk

Reading Rockets
This website, dedicated to developing young readers, has loads of poetry resources – just type 'poetry' into the search box and you'll find countless inspiring ideas!

readingrockets.org